PROMISES
OF
SCRIPTURE

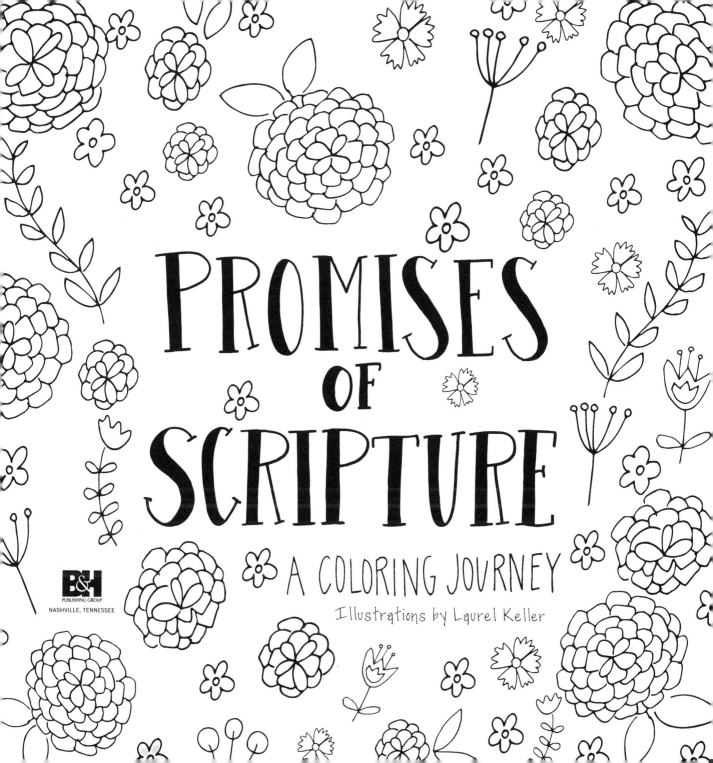

PROMISES OF SCRIPTURE

A COLORING JOURNEY

Illustrations by Laurel Keller

B&H
PUBLISHING GROUP
NASHVILLE, TENNESSEE

978-1-4336-4921-9

Published by B&H Publishing Group
Nashville, Tennessee

Custom printing for LifeWay Christian Stores.

1 2 3 4 5 6 7 8 • 21 20 19 18 17 16

CONTENTS

Genesis 28:15—Look, **I am with you and will watch over you wherever you go.** I will bring you back to this land, for I will not leave you until I have done what I have promised you.

Exodus 14:14—**The Lord will fight for you**; you must be quiet.

Leviticus 26:12—**I will walk among you and be your God, and you will be My people.**

Deuteronomy 4:31—He will not leave you, destroy you, or forget the covenant with your fathers that He swore to them by oath, because **the Lord your God is a compassionate God**.

Deuteronomy 28:12—**The Lord will open for you His abundant storehouse**, the sky, to give your land rain in its season and to bless all the work of your hands. You will lend to many nations, but you will not borrow.

Deuteronomy 31:8—**The Lord is the One who will go before you. He will be with you; He will not leave you or forsake you.** Do not be afraid or discouraged.

Joshua 1:9—Haven't I commanded you: be strong and courageous? **Do not be afraid or discouraged, for the Lord your God is with you wherever you go.**

Joshua 23:14—I am now going the way of all the earth, and you know with all your heart and all your soul that **none of the good promises the Lord your God made to you has failed**. Everything was fulfilled for you; not one promise has failed.

2 Samuel 22:33–34—God is my strong refuge; **He makes my way perfect. He makes my feet like the feet of a deer and sets me securely on the heights**.

Psalms 9:9—**The Lord is a refuge for the oppressed, a refuge in times of trouble.**

Psalm 9:10—Those who know Your name trust in You because **You have not abandoned those who seek You,** Yahweh.

Psalm 23:2—**He lets me lie down in green pastures**; He leads me beside quiet waters.

Psalms 32:8—**I will instruct you and show you the way to go; with My eye on you, I will give counsel.**

Psalms 34:17—**The righteous cry out, and the Lord hears, and delivers them from all their troubles.**

Psalm 34:18—The Lord is near the brokenhearted; **He saves those crushed in spirit.**

Psalm 37:24—Though he falls, **he will not be overwhelmed, because the Lord holds his hand.**

Psalm 48:14—**This God, our God forever and ever—He will always lead us.**

Psalms 50:15—Call on Me in a day of trouble; I will rescue you, and you will honor Me.

Psalms 61:3—**You have been a refuge for me, a strong tower in the face of the enemy.**

Psalm 62:2—**He alone is my rock and my salvation, my stronghold**; I will never be shaken.

Psalm 84:11—**For the Lord God is a sun and shield.** The Lord gives grace and glory; He does not withhold the good from those who live with integrity.

Psalm 97:10—You who love the Lord, hate evil! **He protects the lives of His godly ones**; He rescues them from the power of the wicked.

Psalm 146:9—**The Lord protects foreigners and helps the fatherless and the widow**, but He frustrates the ways of the wicked.

Psalm 145:13—Your kingdom is an everlasting kingdom; Your rule is for all generations. **The Lord is faithful in all His words and gracious in all His actions.**

Psalm 146:7—Executing justice for the exploited and giving food to the hungry. **The Lord frees prisoners.**

Psalm 147:3—**He heals the brokenhearted and binds up their wounds.**

Proverbs 1:33—But **whoever listens to me will live securely and be free from the fear of danger.**

Isaiah 40:31—**Those who trust in the Lord will renew their strength; they will soar on wings like eagles; they will run and not grow weary; they will walk and not faint.**

Isaiah 41:10—Do not fear, for I am with you; **do not be afraid, for I am your God. I will strengthen you; I will help you**; I will hold on to you with My righteous right hand.

Isaiah 41:13—For I, Yahweh your God, hold your right hand and say to you: **Do not fear, I will help you.**

Isaiah 44:3—For I will pour water on the thirsty land and streams on the dry ground; **I will pour out My Spirit on your descendants and My blessing on your offspring.**

Isaiah 44:22—I have swept away your transgressions like a cloud, and your sins like a mist. Return to Me, for I have redeemed you.

Isaiah 46:4a—I will be the same until your old age, and I will bear you up when you turn gray.

Isaiah 46:4b—I have made you, and I will carry you; I will bear and save you.

Isaiah 46:10—I declare the end from the beginning, and from long ago what is not yet done, saying: **My plan will take place, and I will do all My will.**

Isaiah 54:10—"Though the mountains move and the hills shake, **My love will not be removed from you and My covenant of peace will not be shaken,**" says your compassionate Lord.

Isaiah 54:17—"**No weapon formed against you will succeed**, and you will refute any accusation raised against you in court. This is the heritage of the Lord's servants, and their righteousness is from Me." This is the Lord's declaration.

Isaiah 65:24—Even **before they call, I will answer**; while they are still speaking, I will hear.

Jeremiah 1:5—I chose you before I formed you in the womb; I set you apart before you were born. I appointed you a prophet to the nations.

Jeremiah 15:21—I will deliver you from the power of evil people and redeem you from the control of the ruthless.

Jeremiah 29:13—You will seek Me and find Me when you search for Me with all your heart.

Jeremiah 33:3—Call to Me and I will answer you and tell you great and incomprehensible things you do not know.

Lamentations 3:22—Because of the Lord's faithful love we do not perish, for His mercies never end.

Ezekiel 34:12—As a shepherd looks for his sheep on the day he is among his scattered flock, **so I will look for My flock. I will rescue them from all the places where they have been scattered on a cloudy and dark day.**

Ezekiel 36:26–27—I will give you a new heart and put a new spirit within you; **I will remove your heart of stone and give you a heart of flesh.**

Joel 2:28—After this **I will pour out My Spirit on all humanity**; then your sons and your daughters will prophesy, your old men will have dreams, and your young men will see visions.

Malachi 3:6—"**Because I, Yahweh, have not changed**, you descendants of Jacob have not been destroyed."

Matthew 5:4—**Those who mourn are blessed, for they will be comforted.**

Matthew 11:28—**Come to Me, all of you who are weary and burdened, and I will give you rest.**

Matthew 25:34—Then the King will say to those on His right, "Come, you who are blessed by My Father, **inherit the kingdom prepared for you from the foundation of the world.**"

Luke 11:9—So I say to you, keep asking, and it will be given to you. Keep searching and you will find. **Keep knocking, and the door will be opened to you.**

John 3:34—For God sent Him, and He speaks God's words, since **He gives the Spirit without measure.**

John 8:36—Therefore, **if the Son sets you free, you really will be free.**

John 10:29—My Father, who has given them to Me, is greater than all. **No one is able to snatch them out of the Father's hands.**

John 14:27—Peace I leave with you. **My peace I give to you.** I do not give to you as the world gives. Your heart must not be troubled or fearful.

Romans 8:1—Therefore, **no condemnation now exists for those in Christ Jesus.**

Romans 8:28—We know that **all things work together for the good of those who love God**: those who are called according to His purpose.

1 Corinthians 6:18—"**I will be a Father to you**, and you will be sons and daughters to Me," says the Lord Almighty.

1 Corinthians 10:13—No temptation has overtaken you except what is common to humanity. God is faithful, and **He will not allow you to be tempted beyond what you are able**, but with the temptation He will also provide a way of escape so that you are able to bear it.

1 Corinthians 13:8—**Love never ends.** But as for prophecies, they will come to an end; as for languages, they will cease; as for knowledge, it will come to an end.

2 Corinthians 1:20—For **every one of God's promises is "Yes" in Him.** Therefore, the "Amen" is also spoken through Him by us for God's glory.

2 Corinthians 3:17—Now the Lord is the Spirit, and **where the Spirit of the Lord is, there is freedom.**

2 Corinthians 5:1—For we know that if our temporary, earthly dwelling is destroyed, **we have a building from God, an eternal dwelling in the heavens**, not made with hands.

2 Corinthians 5:17—Therefore, **if anyone is in Christ, he is a new creation**; old things have passed away, and look, new things have come.

2 Corinthians 12:9—But He said to me, "**My grace is sufficient for you, for power is perfected in weakness.**" Therefore, I will most gladly boast all the more about my weaknesses, so that Christ's power may reside in me.

Galatians 3:29—And **if you belong to Christ, then you are** Abraham's seed, **heirs according to the promise.**

Ephesians 1:13—When you heard the message of truth, the gospel of your salvation, and when you believed in Him, **you were also sealed with the promised Holy Spirit.**

Philippians 1:6—I am sure of this, that **He who started a good work in you will carry it on to completion until the day of Christ Jesus.**

Philippians 2:13—For **it is God who is working in you**, enabling you both to desire and to work out His good purpose.

Philippians 4:13—**I am able to do all things through Him who strengthens me.**

Philippians 4:19—And **my God will supply all your needs according to His riches in glory in Christ Jesus.**

2 Thessalonians 3:16—**May the Lord of peace Himself give you peace** always in every way. The Lord be with all of you.

Hebrews 10:23—Let us hold on to the confession of our hope without wavering, for **He who promised is faithful**.

Hebrews 13:5—Your life should be free from the love of money. Be satisfied with what you have, for He Himself has said, **I will never leave you or forsake you.**

James 4:7—Therefore, submit to God. But **resist the Devil, and he will flee from you**.

James 4:8—**Draw near to God, and He will draw near to you.** Cleanse your hands, sinners, and purify your hearts, double-minded people!

1 Peter 5:7—Casting all your care on Him, because **He cares about you.**

2 Peter 1:3—**His divine power has given us everything required for life and godliness** through the knowledge of Him who called us by His own glory and goodness.

2 Peter 1:4—By these **He has given us very great and precious promises**, so that through them you may share in the divine nature, escaping the corruption that is in the world because of evil desires.

1 John 1:9—If we confess our sins, **He is faithful and righteous to forgive us** our sins and to cleanse us from all unrighteousness.

1 John 3:1—**Look at how great a love the Father has given us that we should be called God's children.** And we are! The reason the world does not know us is that it didn't know Him.

1 John 4:16—And we have come to know and to believe the love that God has for us. **God is love**, and the one who remains in love remains in God, and God remains in him.

1 John 5:14—Now this is the confidence we have before Him: **Whenever we ask anything according to His will, He hears us.**

Revelation 3:20—Listen! **I stand at the door and knock. If anyone hears My voice and opens the door, I will come in to him** and have dinner with him, and he with Me.

INTRODUCTION

Growing up, everyone enjoys coloring. Then, at some point along the way, we decide that we should not be spending our time in such a childish way. The sad part is, coloring has strong benefits for all ages, and is anything but childish.

Give your mind a break! Today it is all about the rush. Bouncing from one activity to another, all the while thinking about the worries of tomorrow. Our brains have become computers with so many tabs open it's hard to remember what should be your focus. Coloring gives your mind a chance to process through what has been on your mind, and actually close tabs that you have been holding open.

Train your brain! Teachers do not just give children coloring pages to have fun. Coloring—especially within the lines—improves fine motor skills, and strengthens attention to detail. These are not things that we learn once and have perfect forever. These are skills that we need to be constantly training, not only to grow, but to even hold on to the abilities that we have.

Lose the anxiety! Psychiatrist Carl Jung, the founder of analytical psychology, would prescribe coloring pages to his patients. It would help them to release stress and anxiety that would otherwise overwhelm them. This is a practice that is still used, and one that we can self prescribe! Stress looks different on different people. What we all have in common is the need for an outlet to release the stress that builds up. Coloring fills this need and supplies a safe release of pent up tension.

Be creative! Not everyone is a gifted painter, but everyone has some form of creativity that needs to be expressed. Coloring pages give an opportunity for those of all levels of artistic ability to express their creativity. You may never have your work hang in an art gallery, but the fridge has no age or skill requirements.

Have fun! When did "because it's fun" become an unacceptable way to spend time? Life needs balance. Whether you enjoy the time alone with your book and colored pencils, or you make a night of it with your friends, coloring is a chance to do something you enjoy.

As you work through these pages let it be a time of peace and focused reflection on the promises that God has given us in His Holy Word. As you color in these words and designs, think about the hope you are given, and leave with a renewed endurance for the gospel of Christ.

LOOK, I am with you & WILL WATCH OVER YOU WHEREVER YOU GO I will bring you back to this land. FOR I WILL NOT LEAVE YOU UNTIL I HAVE DONE WHAT I HAVE promised you.

HE WILL **NOT** LEAVE YOU,
DESTROY YOU, OR FORGET
THE *covenant* WITH YOUR
FATHERS THAT HE SWORE
TO THEM BY OATH, BECAUSE
THE *Lord* YOUR *God*
IS A
COMPASSIONATE
— GOD. —

the Lord will OPEN for you His abundant storehouse, THE SKY, to give your land RAIN in its SEASON & to bless ALL the work of your hands. YOU will lend to MANY nations, but you WILL NOT borrow.

GOD IS MY STRONG refuge; HE MAKES MY WAY perfect. HE MAKES MY feet LIKE THE feet OF A DEER & SETS ME SECURELY ON the heights.

THE *Lord* IS A REFUGE for the OPRESSED, A REFUGE IN *times* of trouble. THOSE WHO KNOW *Your name* TRUST IN *You* BECAUSE YOU HAVE NOT ABANDONED THOSE WHO *seek* YOU.

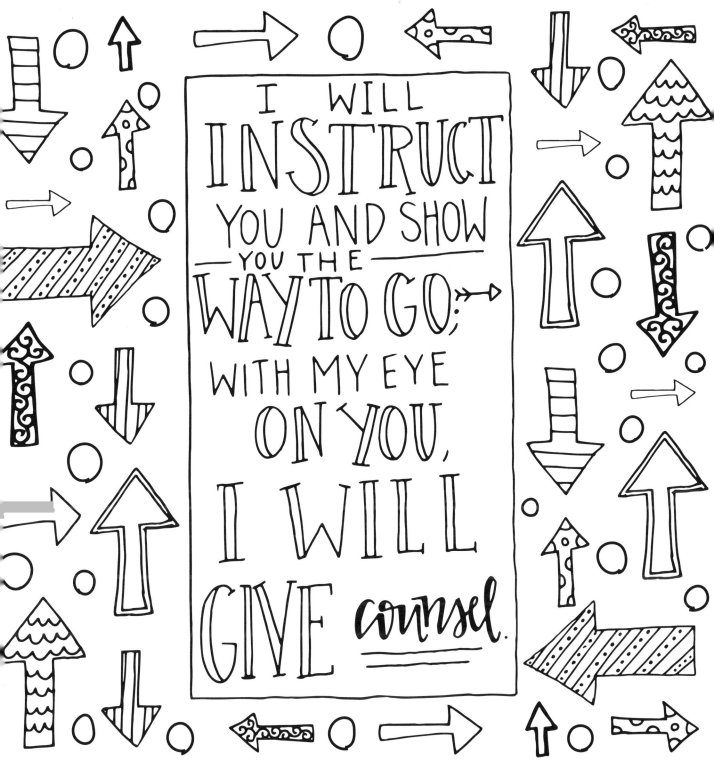

the RIGHTEOUS CRY OUT, & the Lord hears, & DELIVERS them from ALL their TROUBLES.

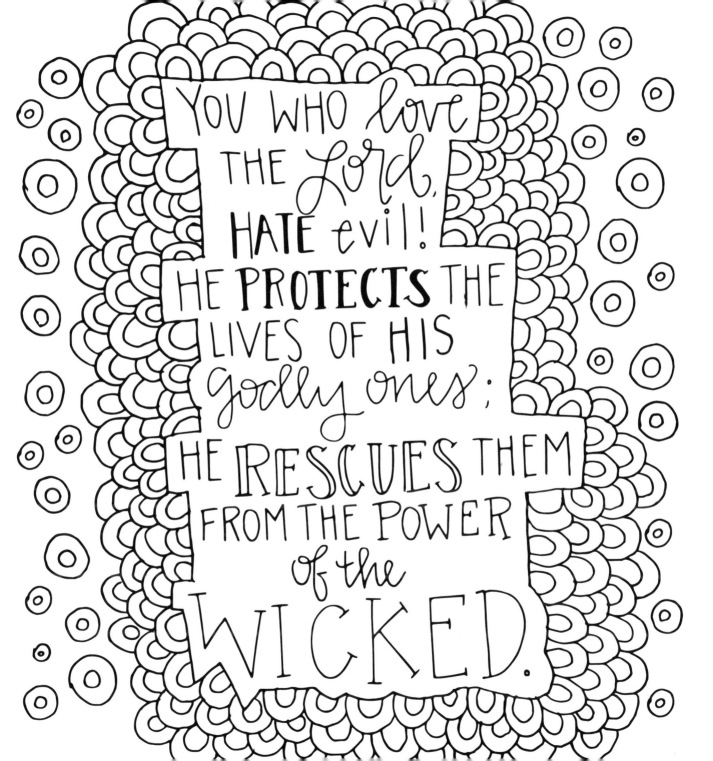

BUT WHOEVER listens TO ME WILL live SECURELY AND BE FREE FROM THE fear OF DANGER.

DO NOT FEAR,
>>> for I am with you;
DO NOT BE AFRAID,
>>> for I am your God.
I WILL STRENGTHEN YOU,
I WILL help YOU;
I will HOLD on to you
with my RIGHTEOUS
right hand.

For I will pour water on the THIRSTY land and streams on the DRY ground; I will pour out My Spirit on your descendants and My blessing on your offspring.

I HAVE swept away YOUR TRANSGRESSIONS LIKE A CLOUD, & YOUR SINS LIKE A MIST. Return to Me, for I have redeemed you.

I DECLARE the END from the BEGINNING, & from LONG AGO what is not yet done, SAYING: My plan will take place, & I will do all My Will.

"NO WEAPON FORMED AGAINST YOU WILL SUCCEED, & you will refute any accusation raised against you in court. This is the HERITAGE of the Lord's servants, & their righteousness is from Me." This is the Lord's declaration.

I will DELIVER you from the POWER of EVIL people & redeem you from the CONTROL of the RUTHLESS.

BECAUSE OF THE *Lord's* FAITHFUL LOVE WE DO NOT PERISH, FOR *His* *mercies* NEVER *end.*

As a shepherd looks for his sheep on the day he is among his scattered flock, so I will look for My flock. I will rescue them from all the places where they have been scattered on a cloudy & dark day.

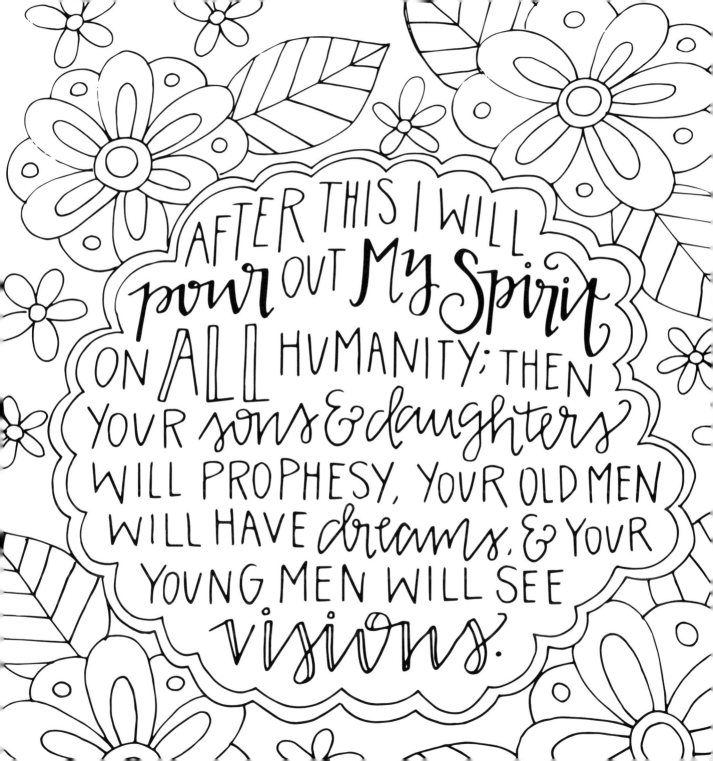

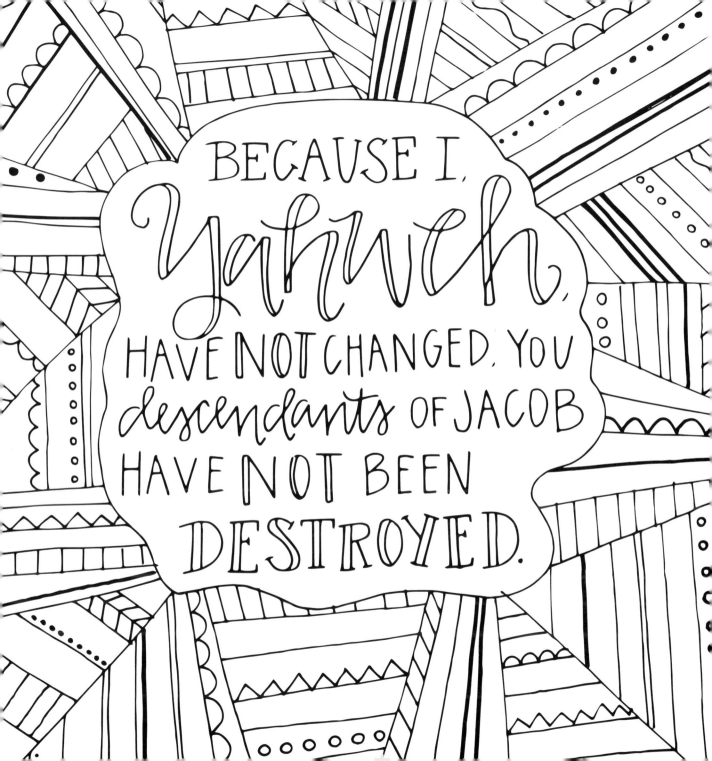

BECAUSE I, Yahweh, HAVE NOT CHANGED. YOU descendants OF JACOB HAVE NOT BEEN DESTROYED.

Then the KING will say to those on His RIGHT, "Come, you who are blessed by MY FATHER, inherit THE KINGDOM prepared for you from the FOUNDATION of the WORLD."

So I say to you, KEEP ASKING, & it will be given to you; KEEP SEARCHING & you will find & the door opened you. KEEP KNOCKING will be to

My Father, who has GIVEN them to ME, is GREATER than ALL. No one is ABLE to SNATCH them out of THE Father's hands.

I WILL BE A *Father* TO YOU, AND YOU WILL BE *Sons & daughters* TO ME, SAYS THE *Lord* ALMIGHTY

NO TEMPTATION HAS OVERTAKEN YOU EXCEPT WHAT IS COMMON TO HUMANITY. GOD IS FAITHFUL & HE WILL NOT ALLOW YOU TO BE TEMPTED BEYOND WHAT YOU ARE ABLE, BUT WITH THE TEMPTATION HE WILL ALSO PROVIDE A WAY OF ESCAPE SO THAT YOU ARE ABLE TO BEAR IT.

Now the Lord is the Spirit, & where the Spirit of the Lord is there is FREEDOM.

FOR WE KNOW THAT IF OUR *temporary,* EARTHLY DWELLING IS DESTROYED, WE HAVE A BUILDING FROM GOD, AN *eternal,* DWELLING IN THE *heavens,* NOT MADE WITH HANDS.

THEREFORE, IF *anyone* is in CHRIST, HE IS A *new creation;* OLD THINGS HAVE PASSED AWAY, & *look,* NEW *things* HAVE COME.

AND IF YOU *belong* TO CHRIST, THEN YOU ARE *Abraham's* SEED, *heirs* A·C·C·O·R·D·I·N·G TO THE *promise.*

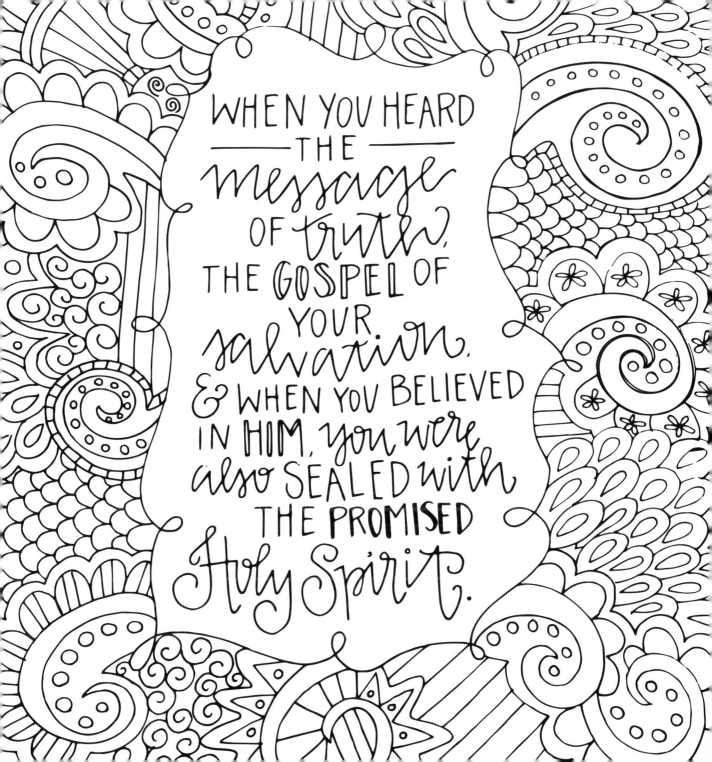

WHEN YOU HEARD
— THE —
message
OF *truth,*
THE GOSPEL OF
YOUR
salvation,
& WHEN YOU BELIEVED
IN HIM, *you were*
also SEALED *with*
THE PROMISED
Holy Spirit.

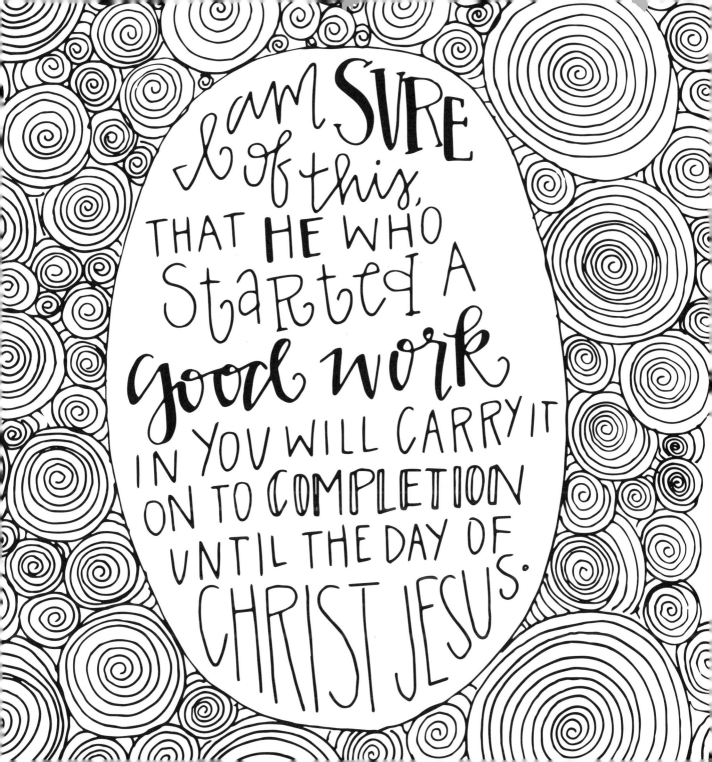

For it is God who is working in you, ENABLING you both to DESIRE & to WORK OUT His Good purpose.

Let us hold on to the confession of our HOPE without wavering, for He who promised is FAITHFUL.

Your life SHOULD BE FREE from the love of MONEY. BE satisfied WITH WHAT YOU HAVE, FOR HE HIMSELF HAS SAID, I will never leave you or forsake you.

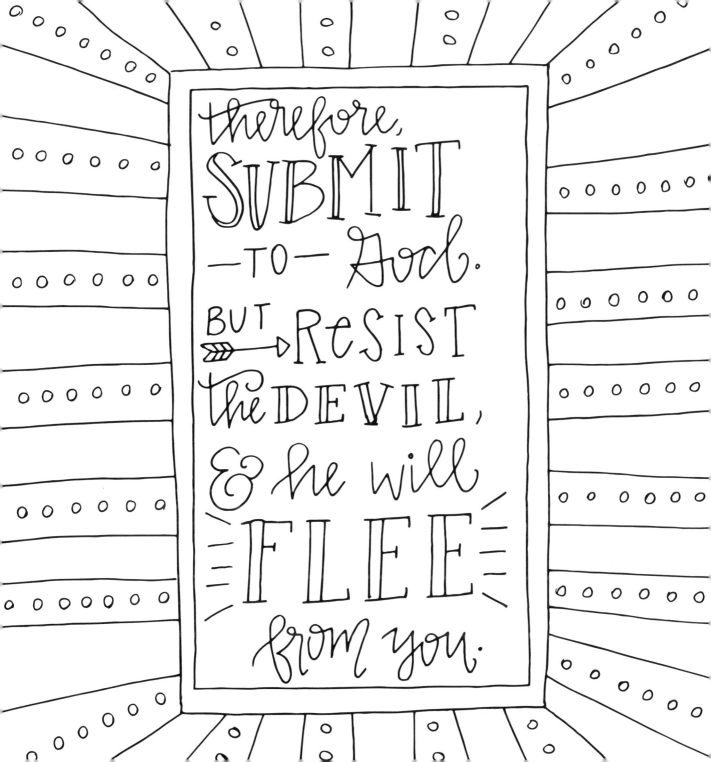

— HIS —
divine POWER
has GIVEN us
every thing REQUIRED
FOR LIFE & GODLINESS
through the KNOWLEDGE
OF HIM WHO CALLED US BY
His OWN GLORY &
goodness.

By these He has given us very GREAT & PRECIOUS promises, so that through them you may share in the divine nature, escaping the corruption that is in the world because of evil desires.

IF WE CONFESS OUR SINS, HE IS *faithful* AND RIGHTEOUS TO FORGIVE US OUR SINS AND TO CLEANSE US FROM ALL *unrighteous*NESS

LOOK AT HOW GREAT
A LOVE THE FATHER
HAS GIVEN US THAT
WE SHOULD BE CALLED
GOD'S
children.
AND WE ARE!
THE REASON THE
WORLD DOES NOT
KNOW US IS THAT
IT DIDN'T KNOW
HIM.

AND WE HAVE come to know AND TO believe THE **LOVE** THAT GOD HAS FOR US. GOD IS love, AND THE ONE WHO REMAINS IN love REMAINS IN GOD, & GOD REMAINS IN him.

Now this is THE CONFIDENCE we have before HIM: whenever we ASK anything ACCORDING to HIS will, HE hears US.

Listen! I STAND AT THE DOOR & KNOCK. If anyone hears MY voice & opens the door, I will COME in to him & have DINNER with him, & he with ME.

ABOUT THE ILLUSTRATOR

Laurel Keller lives in Nashville, Tennessee, but is originally from Georgia. She has always had a deep love of art and connecting it to God's Word. In addition to painting and drawing, she loves reading and spending time with her husband, Jake, and their dog, Hooper. She also letters and creates hand-made pieces at her shop Anchor and Gail Designs.

Instagram: @anchorandgaildesigns
Facebook: @anchorandgail